Telling Even More Tales

INTERACTIVE BIBLE STORIES AND READINGS FOR ALL AGES

Dave & Lynn Hopwood

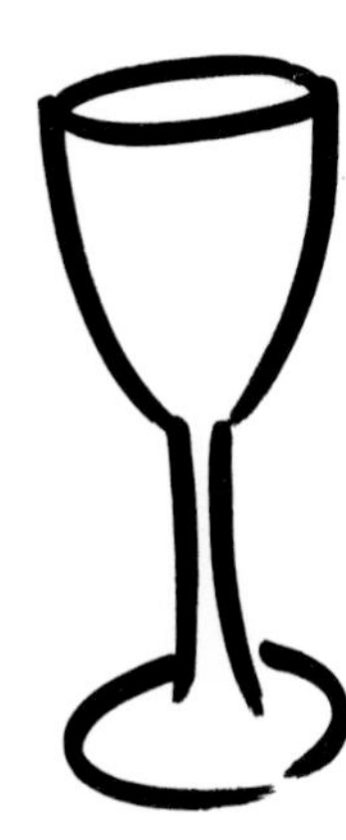

First edition 2000

Published by CPAS
Athena Drive
Tachbrook Park
WARWICK
CV34 6NG

Church Pastoral Aid Society
Registered Charity No 1007820
A company limited by guarantee

Cover design by Wild Associates
Illustrations by Lynn Hopwood
Cover illustrations by Gill Wild
Printed by Unigraph Printing Services
Consultant: Alastair Duncan

ISBN 1 902041 11 9
British Library Cataloguing-in-Publication Data
A catalogue record for this book is available from the British Library

CONTENTS

Story	Bible reference/details	Page
Old Testament		
Creation	Genesis 1	5
What's in a Name?	Genesis 5 & 6: Methuselah	6
Abraham and Sarah	Genesis 15 & 18	7
Sodom and Gomorrah	Genesis 19	8
Abraham and Isaac	Genesis 22	9
Jacob's Wrestling Match	Genesis 32	10
Frisk and Dexter and the Well Boy	Genesis 37: Joseph	11
Moses Runs Away	Exodus 2	12
Ten Good Rules	Exodus 20	13
Samuel in the Temple	1 Samuel 3	14
Queen Esther	Esther	15
Job's Troubles	Job	16
Jeremiah and the Potter	Jeremiah 18	17
Louder than Words	Ezekiel	18
Daniel in the Lions' Den	Daniel 6	19
New Testament		
The Shepherds	Matthew/Luke 1 & 2	20
Christmas Crowd Story	Matthew/Luke 1 & 2	21
When He Appeared	Matthew/Luke 1 & 2	22
Jesus in the Temple	Luke 2	23
Talking to God	Matthew 6: The Lord's Prayer	24
Jesus Spoils a Funeral	Luke 7: The Raising of the Widow's Son	25
Up the Mountain	Luke 9: The Transfiguration	26
Teaching, Healing, Miracles and Stories	Luke 9 & 10	27
A Good Harvest	Matthew 13: The Sower	28
The Parable of the Lost Golf Ball	Luke 15: The Lost Coin	29
The Parable of the Net	Matthew 13	30
Good Sam	Luke 10: The Good Samaritan	31
Zacchaeus	Luke 19	32
The Shopping Trip	Luke 15: The Lost Sheep	33
Lots of Miracle Men	Luke 20	34
Doing Their Best	Matthew 25: The Parable of the Talents	35
The Widow's Mite	Mark 12	36
The Triumphal Entry	Matthew 21	37
Palm Sunday Crowd Story	Matthew 21	38
Communion Rap	Matthew 26	39
Good Friday	Matthew 27 & Luke 23	40
The Commission	Acts 1: The Ascension	41
The Day of Pentecost	Acts 2	42
Saul and the Bright Light	Acts 9	43
Paul's Narrow Escape	Acts 9	44
The Prison Breakout	Acts16	45
Putting on the Armour	Ephesians 6	46
Other Stories		
This Ol' Earth	Looking after the World	47
A Purple Patch	Money	48

INTRODUCTION

Response stories are pieces that involve the whole audience (and the whole family); they are dramatic stories that can be used with little rehearsal or preparation. Each story contains a selection of key words or phrases that are repeated at different points throughout the story. Whenever the audience or congregation hear the key words they should respond with the appropriate noise or action. A narrator can deliver the story alone or a whole group may lead the responses from the front – such a group may be rehearsed or spontaneous. You may like to write down the responses on large cards that the group members hold up whenever each key word occurs.

It is important when telling the story to adopt a fairly animated style. Don't be afraid to stop and encourage the audience if they start flagging. The material for some of the stories has been lifted straight from the Bible as in *The Triumphal Entry*; in others the material has been modernized and paraphrased as in the case of *The Parable of the Lost Golf Ball*. Before beginning the story take time to explain all the key words and responses clearly, as it can be frustrating for both the narrator and the audience if people long to join in but haven't quite grasped the whole picture.

This book contains forty-four of these pieces, but similar sketches can easily be created. Why not have a go yourself? Any Bible story, parable, or theme can be brought to life and understood with this simple style of presentation. A balance needs to be struck with the key words so that they are used frequently enough to keep the attention of the audience but not so often that they become boring. It may also be helpful if one or two of the words relate in some way to the point of the story, as it is these words that the audience is most likely to remember afterwards. (Sometimes it is a good idea to engage a part of the audience in competition with another: for example, to see who can make the most noise!)

So – got the idea? Why not give it a try? These stories are excellent material for all-age services, school assemblies or Sunday schools, and they are also good 'up the sleeve' routines for unexpected situations. Also, any of the pieces contained within this book may be used simply as straight stories without audience participation. No licence need be obtained however they are used.

Stage directions

The stage directions given for each response are extremely brief. Usually if they are in speech marks then the audience should say these lines, for example in *The Commission*: **Gift** – 'It's for you!' You might like to embellish these: for example, in this case holding out a mimed present as you say it. In some of the stories you will need to divide the audience into sections and allocate each section a different response, as in *Good Sam*, allocating rival football teams; or allocate the different sections a different character, as in *Job's Troubles*. Sometimes this is simply a case of each section standing when they hear their particular character named in the story. At other times a specific action or vocal response is required. Often I have left it to your discretion as to how you use the responses. You may like to ask everyone to do exactly the same noise at times, or you may ask everyone to make his or her own individual noise. Having said this, it is always helpful to suggest and demonstrate the responses, to give the audience the right idea. If you simply ask them to make, say, animal sounds, they may have no idea what to do and might subsequently just sit quietly in their seats for the duration of the story. Never force anyone to join in, for some it is more enjoyable and less threatening simply to observe others. Leading by example is the best way to encourage an enthusiastic response. Try and be as animated as you can as you teach the responses and tell the story.

THE OLD TESTAMENT

Genesis 1

CREATION

In the beginning, way, way back at the dawn of time, there was **chaos**. And God looked down on the **chaos** and thought, '**Hmmm**, time we had some **order**.' So he took a deep **breath**, snapped his **fingers** and turned the **chaos** into **order**.

Then he looked down on the **order** and thought, '**Hmmm**, it's a bit dark. Time we had some light.' So he took a deep **breath**, snapped his **fingers** and turned the darkness into light.

Then he looked down on the light and saw there was lots of water, and he thought, '**Hmmm**, it's a bit **empty**. Time we had some sky.' So he took a deep **breath**, snapped his **fingers** and turned some of the light into sky.

Then he looked down on the water and thought, '**Hmmm**, it's a bit wet. Time we had some dry land.' So he took a deep **breath**, snapped his **fingers** and turned some of the water into dry land.

Then he looked down on the land and thought, '**Hmmm**, it's a bit **empty**. Time we had some trees.' So he took a deep **breath**, snapped his **fingers** and turned the land into forests.

Then he looked down on the forests and thought, '**Hmmm**, it's a bit **empty**. Time we had some animals.' So he took a deep **breath**, snapped his **fingers** and filled the forests with animals.

'**Wow**!' he said. 'They're good!' So he filled the sea with fish and the sky with birds.

Then he looked down on the animals, fish and birds and thought, '**Hmmm**, time we had some humans.'

So he took a very, very, very deep **breath**, snapped his **fingers**, grabbed a handful of mud, swished it around, blew on it and said, '**Wow**! That's even better.' And there standing on the earth, right in the middle of the forest, right in the middle of the animals, was a man.

And God said, '**Hmmm**, he's a bit lonely. Time we made another one of those.'

So he took a very, very, very, very, very deep **breath**, snapped his **fingers** and made the man fall asleep. Then he ripped out one of his ribs and used it to make a woman.

'**Wow**!' said God. 'Now that finishes it off perfectly.' And God sat back, took a rest and said, 'Now that's what I call creation.' ❑

STAGE DIRECTIONS

Chaos
shout 'Ahh!' and pull at your ears and hair

Order
all adopt very big smiles indeed

Fingers
snap fingers

Breath
breathe in deeply and noisily

Hmmm
scratch head

Wow!
punch the air and shout 'Wow!'

Empty
look all around: up, down, in front, behind

Genesis 5 & 6

WHAT'S IN A NAME?

STAGE DIRECTIONS

Methuselah
scratch head, puzzled

Lala/Dipsy
'Eh oh!'

Mr Blobby
'Blobby, Blobby, Blobby!'

Horrible
'Ugh!'

Worse
'Haaaa!' shocked

Special
hold up finger and say 'Ding!'

Name
each person call out own name

Hammer/Saw/Chisel
divide group into three: some hammer, some saw, some chisel

Noise
all hammer, saw and chisel together

Friends
pat person next to you on the back or arm

Once upon a time there was a man called **Methuselah**. The name means: 'When he is dead it shall be sent.' **Methuselah**. Strange, isn't it? Now, **Methuselah** lived way back in the early days of the Bible. His dad was called Enoch, and Enoch and God were the best of **friends**.

Well, when **Methuselah** was a little boy a lot of people must have wondered about his **name**. **Methuselah**, they would say, that's a funny **name**! And **Methuselah** might have said, well it could be worse, it could have been **Lala**, or **Dipsy** or **Mr Blobby**.

When **Methuselah** grew up he got married and had a little boy of his own called Lamech. In those days people weren't very nice, in fact they were **horrible**, and as the years went by they got **worse**, and **worse**, and **worse**. **Methuselah** and his son were very good **friends** with God, but not many other people were. Up in heaven God began to think of a plan.

Lamech grew up, married and had a son of his own. By now, grandfather **Methuselah** was getting old. He was 369. Is anybody here today 369? Perhaps a few of us feel it. Well, the years rolled by, and the people were still **horrible**. Things got worse and worse. Then one day God said, Enough is enough. I love all the people I've made but this can't go on getting **worse**. I need to find a good carpenter.

Lamech's son was a good carpenter and so God gave him a special job. He set to work **hammering**, **sawing** and **chiselling** and generally making an awful lot of **noise**. When he'd finished **hammering**, **sawing** and **chiselling** – bingo! – he'd made a boat!

His old grandfather **Methuselah**, came to see it and was very proud of his grandson. It was **Methuselah's** birthday. He had reached the ripe old age of 969. God looked down from heaven and said, Well, I've kept you alive, **Methuselah**, for a long, long time – longer than any other person because I didn't want to send my judgement on the planet, but the people just won't take any notice and the time has finally come.

That day **Methuselah** died. And it started raining. So **Methuselah's** grandson, who was called Noah, took his family and lots of animals aboard the new boat, and God flooded the world and gave it a good wash. And that's why **Methuselah** turned out to be the oldest man who ever lived, because as long as he was alive God would not send his judgement on the people, but as soon as he was dead the flood came. God really didn't want to send the flood, so he kept **Methuselah** alive as long as possible, but in the end there was just no other way out. And then his **name** turned out to be true: When he is dead, it shall be sent. **Methuselah**. ❑

A long time ago there was a man called Abraham. He had a wife called Sarah, and lots and lots of animals. Every night Abraham would stand outside and look up at the sky trying to count the **stars**. He would sit on the **sand** with his **dogs** and his **cows**. One night as he was out there with the **stars** and the **sand** and the **dogs** and the **cows**, all of a sudden God appeared and said: 'Abraham, your wife is going to have a **baby**!'

Well, Abraham was so surprised he nearly **laughed** because he and Sarah were very old and it was a shock to think they might have a **baby**. But the Lord told him that nothing is impossible for God and that Abraham and Sarah would have so many relatives that they wouldn't be able to count them all. In fact this one **baby** would become a great nation of people – more than all the **stars**, more than the grains of **sand**, and more than all the **dogs** and **cows**.

Well, Abraham thought about this for a long time. In fact, he thought about it every night as he sat out with the **stars** and the **sand** and the **dogs** and the **cows**. And sometimes he got quite excited about it. But a long, long time went by and he and Sarah still didn't have a **baby**.

Then three visitors came to see him. And while they ate some tea, they said that quite soon Sarah would be a mother. When Sarah heard this she **laughed** and **laughed** and **laughed**. But, sure enough, a year later she had a **baby**!

And from then on, every time they sat outside, Abraham looked at the **stars**, and the **sand**, the **dogs** and the **cows** and he remembered God's promise that one day he and Sarah would be the parents of a great nation. ❑

Genesis 15 & 18

ABRAHAM AND SARAH

STAGE DIRECTIONS

Stars
all look up and shield eyes with hand

Cows
'Moo!'

Dogs
'Woof!'

Baby
all cry

Sand
rub hands

Laughed
laugh

Genesis 19

SODOM AND GOMORRAH

Sometimes we do things **wrong** for all kinds of reasons. Sometimes we do things **wrong** because we can't help it. Sometimes we do things **wrong** because we don't know how to do things right. And sometimes we do things **wrong** because we want to, like in the story of Sodom and Gomorrah.

Sodom and Gomorrah were two cities. But these cities were not **ordinary**. Oh no. They were full of people, but these people were not **ordinary**. Oh no. They did lots of things, but the things they did were not **ordinary**. Oh no.

These people did lots of things **wrong**, not because they couldn't help it, not because they didn't know how to do things right, they did things **wrong** because they wanted to – and that made Sodom and Gomorrah very **scary** places to live in. Very **scary** indeed.

One day God sent a couple of his angels to visit Sodom. They arrived in the city as it was getting dark, and they sat down in the city square. Just then a man called Lot came along. The angels were in disguise and the man didn't know who they were because they looked so **ordinary**. Oh yes.

'Hello,' he said. 'I haven't seen you here before. You're new here aren't you? Want to come to my house for a meal?'
'No, no,' they said. 'We like it here.'
But Lot said, 'No, come back to my place.'
But they said, 'No we're fine.'
This went on for some time until the man said, 'Please, pleeease, pleeeeease come back to my place.'
So they went along with him.

They were just sitting down for an evening meal when there was a **thud** on the door. It wasn't a nice gentle tap. Instead it was a very loud **thud**! 'Open the door,' shouted an **angry** voice, 'We've seen those strangers.' One of the angels peeped outside through a crack in the door. They were surrounded by a mob of **angry** men, all shouting. It was very **scary**.

'It's the **bad** guys in the city. They'll do very **bad** things to you,' said Lot. 'No they won't,' said the angel and, pushing the doors wide open, he snapped his fingers and suddenly everyone outside couldn't see! And while the **bad** guys were wandering around, bashing into each other and falling over with a loud **thud**, the angels took Lot and his family, and they ran as fast as they could away from the town. Suddenly they heard the sound of thunder. It was very, very, very **scary**.

'Don't look back,' said the angels. But Lot's wife did look back, and she saw the whole of Sodom being blown up by God. But it was **bad** news for her. As she watched, her whole body turned into salt, and she was frozen there forever. ❑

STAGE DIRECTIONS

Angry
make an angry face and clench fists

Wrong
cover face with hands and peep through fingers

Ordinary
'Really?'

Thud
'Bang!'

Bad
'Oh, oh!

Scary
look scared, eyes wide

Sometimes it's not easy to **understand** God. Like the time he asked Abraham to take his son out for a walk one day. God had asked Abraham to do a very difficult thing, so Abraham said to his son:
'Let's go up that nice **mountain**.'
And Isaac said, 'Great **idea**, Dad.' So off they went.

As they got near the top Abraham said, 'Let's stop at the top and rest for a while.' And Isaac said, 'Great **idea**, Dad.' So up they went.

Up on top of the **mountain** they had an amazing view and Abraham suddenly said, 'I know let's give God a present, a **sacrifice** to tell him how good he is.' And Isaac said, 'Great **idea**, Dad.' So they got some wood together and got ready to set fire to it.

'What shall we use for the **sacrifice**?' Isaac asked. And Abraham remembered the difficult thing that God had asked him to do. With a sad look on his face, he said, 'You!'
And Isaac said, 'Er… great **idea**? Dad?'

Sometimes it's not easy to **understand** God. He had given Abraham a precious son and now he had told Abraham to kill him. It seemed very unfair.

Abraham looked very sad as he lifted Isaac up as a **sacrifice** and laid him gently on the wood. Isaac looked very confused. Then Abraham took out his **knife**, lifted it up in the air and brought it down on Isaac.

'Stop!' yelled a voice, and at the last minute Abraham's **knife** stopped right over Isaac's heart. It was an angel.

'Don't kill the boy,' said the angel. 'Look there's a ram over there you can use that for the **sacrifice**. Now that God can see you are prepared to obey him even to the point of killing your own son, you don't have to do it. Well done, Abraham, you put God first.'

And Abraham killed the ram instead and **sacrificed** that on the fire.

And Isaac said, '**Phew**!' And he looked very relieved. ❑

Genesis 22

ABRAHAM AND ISAAC

STAGE DIRECTIONS

Mountain
look up, with hand above eyes

Understand
scratch head and say 'Mmm?'

Knife
look up, shocked

Phew!
'Phew!'

Idea
slap leg

Sacrifice/d
hold out hands, palms upwards, as if holding up a sacrifice

Genesis 32

JACOB'S WRESTLING MATCH

Jacob had a brother; **Esau** was his name.
They didn't get on very well; they just weren't the same.

Jacob was a gentle man; **Esau** was rough and toothy.
Esau was a hairy man; **Jacob** was a smoothie.

Esau was his **father's** favourite; **Jacob** was his **mother's**.
Jacob's mum persuaded him to pinch what was his **brother's**.

Jacob went to see his **dad**, disguised in skin pyjamas.
His **father** gave him a blessing and **Esau** went bananas.

So **Jacob** did a runner, he had to get away.
He left behind the **family** in total disarray.

Years went by and before too long a **wife** or two he had.
He also had eleven **sons**, and they all called him **dad**.

It was time to go back home, though **Jake** was terrified:
The last time he saw **Esau**, he'd threatened fratricide.... Er, what's fratricide?
(*Ask audience, then continue.*)

The night before they met – a strange thing came to pass,
God came to earth for **Jacob** and they had a wrestling match.

All night long the fight went on, but **Jacob** wouldn't slip.
As dawn approached God said, 'Let go,' and struck him on the hip.

'Your name will not be **Jacob**. It's Israel from now on.
You've wrestled with both man and God. I'm surprised to say you've won.'

And God blessed **Jacob** there and then, and **Jacob** knelt and said,
'Wow! I have met God face to face and I should now be dead.'

Then **Jacob** left that place and went limping on his way,
And **Esau**, when 'e saw his **brother**, he didn't blow him away.

The two forgave each other and went back home that night.
'Where'd you get that limp?' asked **Esau**, and **Jacob** said, 'A fight.' ❑

STAGE DIRECTIONS

Jacob/Jake
all girls stand

Esau
all boys stand

Father/Dad
all fathers stand

Mother
all mothers stand

Wife
all married women stand

Brother
all brothers stand

Sons
all sons stand

Family
everyone stand

Deliberately mispronounce *smoothie* in verse two so that it rhymes with *toothy.*

Frisk and Dexter ran a time-travel investigation agency. They were detectives who could investigate any crime from any time. When the purple phone rang like an old school bell, they knew that a case from history was calling them. Dexter wore a long black **coat** and had a dog called Bilko. Frisk wore dark glasses and always carried a **notebook**.

One day the purple phone rang. Frisk and Dexter found themselves sweating in the middle of a desert. Frisk was grateful for his dark glasses as the sun beat down like a massive spotlight, but Dexter threw off his long black **coat** and left it lying in the dust. They began to walk.

'Where now, Boss?' asked Frisk, flicking open his **notebook** and beginning to scribble in it.

'Listen!' Dexter stopped. Frisk walked into him. Bilko walked into Frisk.

'Shhh!' said Dexter. They heard a cry. Frisk pointed to an old muddy **well** and they ran towards it like kids running for an ice-cream van. They stopped and looked in. A young teenager lay at the bottom, his body crunched up and splashes of blood smeared on his face and clothes. The situation looked **dangerous**.

'Someone's thrown him in,' whispered Frisk, scribbling in his **notebook**.
'Why are you whispering?' whispered Dexter.

They looked around. The desert was deserted.

'Sorry,' said Frisk, 'thought the guys who threw him in might still be around.'

Dexter tried to reach inside to pull the boy out, but the **well** was too deep.

'Here Boss, try this.' Frisk had picked up Dexter's black **coat**. They lowered it into the **well** for the boy to grab hold of, but it was still too short.
'Nothing else for it,' said Dexter, rolling his sleeves up, 'I'm going in.'
'No wait!' Just as he was about to climb inside, Frisk pointed off into the distance. A long wiry line of camels appeared on the skyline. The riders looked **mean** and **dangerous**.

'No time to waste,' said Dexter. 'If we don't get him, they will.'

But Frisk stopped him again. He pointed down inside the **well**, towards the boy's **coat**. It lay next to him and it was all the **colours** of the rainbow.

'I don't think we should rescue him, Boss,' said Frisk. 'I think this boy's gonna go to Egypt and get a top job in government.' Dexter wasn't so sure. He looked at the **coat** with all its **colours**, then at the line of camels.

'They look **mean**,' he said, 'could be **dangerous**.'
'It'll be all right,' said Frisk. 'Look here come the boy's brothers.'
From nowhere ten men were approaching the **well**.
'Help!' said Dexter. 'Let's get back to the future, quick!'

As they ran back to the twenty-first century, Frisk noted in his book that sometimes it was better to leave things for God to work out. ❑

Genesis 37

FRISK AND DEXTER AND THE WELL BOY

STAGE DIRECTIONS

Mean
'Grrrrr!'

Dangerous
'Oh! Oh!' and look scared

Colours
'Zing!'

Well
squelching mud sound

Coat
pull up collar

Notebook
flick open imaginary notebook

Exodus 2

MOSES RUNS AWAY

Moses was a Prince in Egypt; he was dead, dead rich.
He lived it up in **Pharaoh's** palace without a hitch or glitch.

One day **Moses** went outside, walking round the city.
There were a lot of **workers** working, and the place was not too pretty.

Then he saw a **soldier** hit one of the men at work.
Moses wasn't pleased with this and he went berserk.

Moses ran up to the **soldier**, and hit him on the head.
It hurt his hand, and **Moses** groaned. The **soldier** fell down dead.

The **soldier** lay there in the dirt, dead upon the sand.
Moses was in big trouble, and he had a bad hand.

Moses dug a pit and buried the **soldier** in the sun.
Then he went home to the palace and tried to forget what he'd just done.

Next day **Moses** went out and he saw two **workers** fight,
'Stop that,' said **Moses**. 'Don't argue – that's not right.'

The **workers** took one look at him and started to back away.
'Don't kill us please,' they begged him, 'like that **soldier** yesterday.'

Moses' face went white and his mouth filled with his heart.
Everyone knew what he had done and it wasn't very smart.

'Excuse me,' **Moses** said and he turned and ran away.
He ran and ran and ran and ran and didn't stop all day.

That was the end of **Moses'** career after causing such a rumpus,
He got another job – tending **sheep** and woolly jumpers.

But God was still in charge and things were not all they seemed.
While Moses cared for **lambs** – he was on a training scheme.

Years later **Moses** went back to Egypt and set the **workers** free.
Moses made an awful fuss and he spoilt **Pharaoh's** tea.

God opened up the river Nile and the **workers** ran away.
But **Pharaoh's soldiers**, they got drowned – it wasn't their day. ❑

STAGE DIRECTIONS

Divide audience into five sections, each one representing a different character or set of characters.

Moses
section 1 stand

Pharaoh
section 2 stand

Soldier
section 3 stand

Workers
section 4 stand

Sheep/Lambs
section 5 stand

Exodus 20

TEN GOOD RULES

While Moses was leading the people of Israel across the **desert** they came to a **mountain** and while the people had a rest Moses went up the **mountain** and had a talk with God. And God said, here are **ten good** rules for living well.

Rule number **one**: Nothing and no one is more important than God.

Rule number **two**: Make God number one in your life and let everything else come second.

Number **three**: God's name is special and sacred, don't use it as a swear word.

Number **four**: Remember that one day in seven is God's special day.

Number **five**: Respect your family and those who take care of you.

Number **six**: Don't kill.

Number **seven**: Only sleep with your husband or wife.

Number **eight**: Don't steal.

Number **nine**: Don't tell lies.

Number **ten**: Don't look at what your friend has and wish it were yours.

To sum it all up, love God and treat others the way you would like them to treat you.

God wrote all these things down for Moses whilst he was up the **mountain**. Then Moses went back down the **mountain** to tell the people in the **desert** about the **ten good** rules for living well. ❑

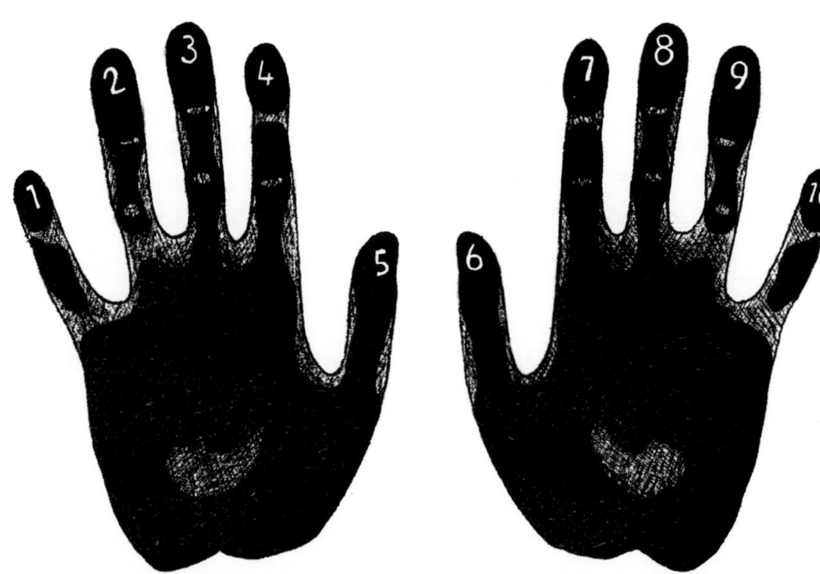

STAGE DIRECTIONS

Desert
fan face and say, 'Are we there yet?'

Mountain
make a mountain shape with hands and arms

Good
make a thumbs-up sign

Any numbers
hold up appropriate number on fingers

1 Samuel 3

SAMUEL IN THE TEMPLE

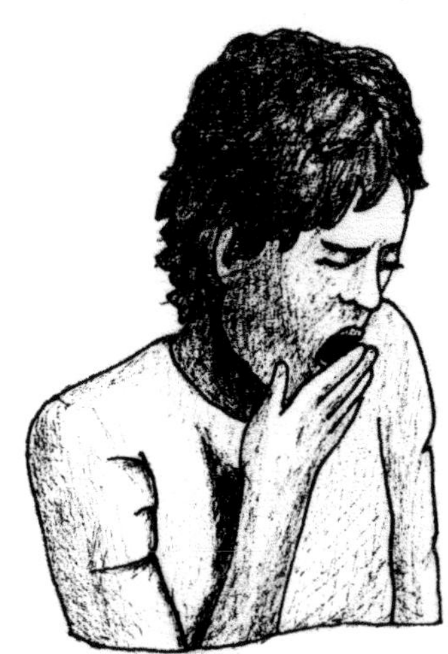

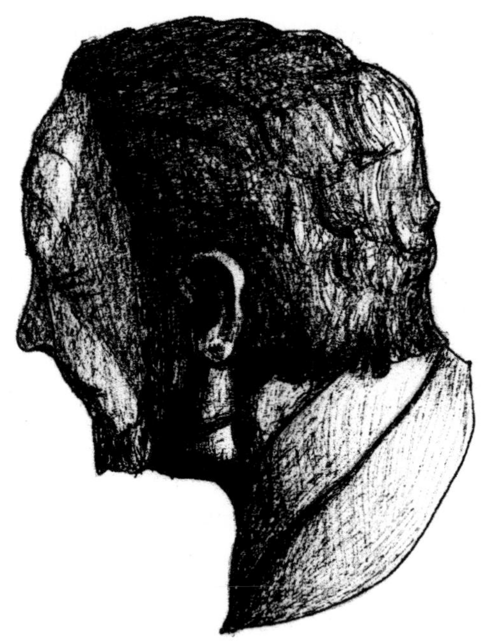

Once upon a time there was a young boy called Samuel. He used to work in the temple, helping Eli who was the priest there. Every night it was Samuel's job to blow out the **candles** on the altar, lock up the front **door**, put the **cat** out the back door. And then he would climb the **stairs** to bed.

Late one night, after he'd blown out the **candles**, locked the **door**, put out the **cat** and climbed the **stairs** to bed, the Lord God spoke to Samuel. This is what he **heard**....

Samuel was amazed when he **heard**.... So he hurried down the **stairs**, checked the **cat**, checked the **door** and checked the **candles**. Then he woke Eli, who said: 'Samuel, do you know what time it is? It's way past your bedtime and you've got to be up early tomorrow. Now go back to bed.'

So Samuel went back up the **stairs** to bed.

Just then he **heard**.... So he hurried back down the **stairs**, checked the **cat**, the **door** and the **candles**. And then he went to Eli, who said: 'Samuel, you're worse than a faulty alarm clock. Go back to bed.'

So Samuel went back up**stairs** to bed. Once again he **heard**....

This time Samuel ran down the **stairs** and went straight to Eli. And this time Eli realized it was the Lord who was calling to Samuel. So Eli said: 'Next time the Lord calls you, tell him you are listening and ask him to speak to you.'

That's exactly what Samuel did, and after that God spoke to him many times. And as he grew older, God used Samuel as a leader to guide and help people. ❑

STAGE DIRECTIONS

Candles
all blow twice

Cat
'Miaow'

Door
'Click, click'

Stairs
footsteps followed by snoring sounds

Heard...
call out 'Samuel!'

QUEEN ESTHER

STAGE DIRECTIONS

Divide the audience into five sections, each section representing one of the characters listed below.

Esther
stand and flutter eyelids

Xerxes
stand with hands on hips, as if in charge

Vashti/Zeresh
'Tut!', unimpressed

Haman
stand and look down nose, snobbishly

Mordecai
stand and stroke chin wisely

Xerxes was a king, a fairly brutal lout.
He said,'My dear wife **Vashti** has turned a little bit nasty,
So I think I'll throw her out.'

So poor old **Vashti** got the boot. King **Xerxes** was not nice.
Then **Xerxes** said,'I'll have a new wife instead.
But I won't make the same mistake twice.'
Xerxes ruled 100 kingdoms, from India to Sudan.
They searched his world for the perfect girl
For this very imperfect man.

Now **Mordecai**, he was a Jew and **Esther** was his niece,
He worked for the king and soon got wind
Of his search for wedded bliss.
Mordecai said,'Listen my young **Esther**, I'd like to propose a motion:
I've foreseen, that you're gonna be queen.
Now that's quite a promotion.'
Esther was quite young, but she also was quite bright.
She went to **Xerxes** with bows and curtsies
And he fell in love at first sight.

Now **Haman** was Prime Minister, he wasn't half a snob.
He said,'My wife **Zeresh**, I no longer cherish
Half as much as my job.'
He also wasn't very keen on **Mordecai** the Jew,
Because when he went by, old **Mordecai**
Didn't bow the way the others would do.

'Right,' he said.'I will not have it. **Mordecai's** bad news.
I'll trick the king into killing him
Along with all the Jews.'
So **Xerxes** signed an order sealing **Mordecai's** fate.
Haman had a grin, but **Zeresh** put in,
'It ain't over yet, just wait.'

When **Mordecai** heard the news he ran to **Esther's** pad,
He fell on his knees and said,'**Esther** please,
King **Xerxes** has gone quite mad.'
Mordecai explained and poor old **Esther** said:
'**Haman's** nasty, bring back **Vashti** –
Let her be queen instead.'

'I can't change anything,' she said,'but I'll do the best I can.'
She fasted and prayed for three whole days
And then she had a plan.
She gave the King a party: **Haman**, and **Zeresh** were there too.
As they got under way, **Esther** started to say,
'King **Xerxes**, **Haman's** tricked you.'

Xerxes was so surprised he backed out through the door.
Haman grabbed **Esther**, tripped up and pressed her
Flat upon the floor.
Xerxes walked back in just then, a snarl upon his lips.
Zeresh tutted, **Xerxes** was gutted.
He said,'**Haman's** had his chips.'

So **Haman** got the chop, his evil plans forsaken.
The Jews all blessed her, good old **Esther** –
She had saved their bacon. ❑

JOB'S TROUBLES

STAGE DIRECTIONS

Divide audience into five sections, each one representing a different character or set of characters.

Job
section one stand

Children
section two stand

Servants
section three stand

Friends
section four stand

Sheep, cows and camels
section five stand

Job lived in the land of Uz.
He was a very rich man.
He had ten **children** and many **servants**,
Cows and **sheep** and land.
They often had big parties.
They'd feast and laugh all night,
But **Job** would always speak to God
In the early morning light.

One afternoon a **servant**
Came running and out of breath.
'We have been attacked,' he said,
'And your **servants** put to death.'
A second **servant** then appeared,
Breathless and covered in mud.
He said,'A storm has killed your **sheep**.
The fields are red with blood.'
Before he could finish talking
Another **servant** came to say,
'A band of rebels attacked from the north
And they've taken your **camels** away.'
Before this one could end his message
A fourth came up and said,
'Sir, a tornado has struck nearby
And all your **children** are dead.'

'This is terrible news,' said **Job**.
'My life's become a ruin.
I don't know why God has allowed this,
But he must know what he's doing
He gave me everything I had,
And now he's taken it away.'
And **Job** went off and prayed to God.
And fell ill the very next day.

But still **Job** would not blame God.
He would not curse or shout.
Some of **Job's friends** heard he was ill
So they came to sort him out.

'God must be very upset,' they said,
'Because of all your sins.'
The **friends** gave lots of reasons
Why things had gone so wrong.
But they didn't know what they were talking about
So they left – and God came along.

'Why has this happened?' said **Job**, at last,
'Why? It's just not fair.
I've lost **children**, **servants**, **sheep** and **cows**
Yet you don't seem to care.'

So God showed **Job** the clouds,
The mountains, sea, and land.
He said,'Did you do all this? I don't think so!
This came from the work of my hand.
I am the creator of all things,
And you are just a man.
And though you're kind and generous,
There are things you can't understand.'

Job was ashamed of his ranting.
He fell down and knelt in the dust.
God said,'I won't give you an answer, **Job**,
But I'll restore everything you have lost.' ❑

Jeremiah 18

JEREMIAH AND THE POTTER

One day Jeremiah was relaxing at home. When suddenly…
There was a **knock** at the door.
It was the Lord.
'Jeremiah,' he said. 'I want a **word** with you.'
And Jeremiah said, 'Who me?'
And the Lord said: 'Yes, I want a **word** with you.'

And the Lord gave Jeremiah some very interesting **instructions**.
He said, 'I want you to go down to the **potter's** house.'
'The **potter's** house?' said Jeremiah.
And the Lord said, 'YES!'
So Jeremiah took note of these **instructions** and off he went.

At the **potter's** house he watched the **potter** at work, moulding his **clay** with his **hands**. Whenever the piece of **clay** he was working with turned out wrong, the potter scrunched it up in his **hands** and threw away the **clay**.

Oh no. I'm sorry. I got that wrong. He didn't throw it away. No.

Instead, he remoulded the **clay** into something else. Something new.

And the Lord said to Jeremiah: 'You are in my **hands**. And I have the right to remould you.' ❑

STAGE DIRECTIONS

Knock
knock on floor or chair

Word
place hand to ear and listen

Instructions
'I see'

Potter/s
watch imaginary potter's wheel go round

Clay
'Splat!' mime throwing lump of clay on a potter's wheel

Hands
pretend to mould with hands

Ezekiel

LOUDER THAN WORDS

Way, way back, a long time ago there was a good old prophet called Ezekiel. He used to tell **people** what God was thinking – but he didn't use words. Oh no, he used to act out the messages that God told him.

One day God told Ezekiel about a battle, so Ezekiel made a model of the town and he acted out the battle.

Another time God told Ezekiel to cut his **hair** and divide the **hair** into three parts. So Ezekiel did that. The three bundles of **hair** were like the **people** and Ezekiel was showing them what would happen to each of them.

Another time God asked Ezekiel to pack a **rucksack** and pretend to sneak out of his house with the **rucksack** as if he was running away. This was to show the people how they would have to escape from the city.

Another time God told Ezekiel to walk around without wearing any **clothes**!

But the strangest thing of all was when God told Ezekiel to make some bread and bake it on a fire made out of human **dung**!

Ezekiel had done lots of things but this time he argued about it, and said, 'I can't do that, Lord. It's horrible, and I'm sure that you would think it's horrible too. I can't believe you **really** want me to do that. Not with human **dung**.'

And God said, '**Really**, I do.'

Ezekiel said, '**Really**?'

And God said, '**Really**.'

And Ezekiel said, '**Really**, **really**, **really**?'

And God said, '**Really**, **really**, **really**.'

In the end God said, 'OK, you can cook it on a fire of cow **dung** instead, if you want. You know, Ezekiel, sometimes I'm prepared to go much further than you think to reach **people**.'

So Ezekiel did all these amazing things to communicate God's message to the **people**, but a lot of them didn't listen. So in the end, years later, God went to the absolute limit to communicate with **people** – he became a man and died for them. ❑

STAGE DIRECTIONS

People
all wave

Dung
'Poo!' wave hand in front of face

Hair
snip, snip

Clothes
'Ha!' shocked

Rucksack
sing: 'Hi ho, hi ho...'

Really
all nod emphatically

Daniel 6

DANIEL IN THE LIONS' DEN

Once upon a time there was a man called **Daniel**. He worshipped God and **prayed** to him three times every day. But the **king**, for whom **Daniel** worked, didn't worship God, or **pray** to him.

And one day, some of the **king's men**, who'd been watching **Daniel**, thought of a plan to get rid of him. The **king's men** didn't like him. So they **went** to the **king** and made him write out an order telling all the people that for one month they must only worship the **king** and no one else. If they disobeyed they would be thrown to the **lions** and eaten.

When **Daniel** heard this, he wasn't worried. He went off to his room to **pray**, three times a day just like he always did.

When the **king's men** found out, they forced the **king** to throw Daniel into the **lions'** den.

But **Daniel** was a man of faith and he believed that God would look after him. And you know what? God did look after him. For one whole night the **lions** never touched **Daniel**. They completely lost their appetites and became vegetarians.

When the **king** saw this, he let **Daniel** out of the **lions'** den, and ordered that everyone should worship God; and pray to him whenever they wanted to. ❑

STAGE DIRECTIONS

Daniel
all cheer

Pray/Prayed
shout 'Amen!'

Lions
roar

King/King's men
'Hissss!'

Went
make the sound of running steps

Matthew/Luke 1 & 2

THE SHEPHERDS

STAGE DIRECTIONS

Shepherds
'Ooh aarr!'

Angel
'Alleluia'

Sheep
'Baa!'

Bright
flick fingers out and say 'Whoosh!'

Stable
sniff twice and say 'Ugh!'

Baby
suck thumb or say 'Aah!'

While **shepherds** watched their **sheep** one night
All seated on the ground,
An **angel** in the sky appeared
And **bright** light shone around.

'Fear not!' The **angel** said, for they were
Scared out of their minds.
'I've got good news – the future's **bright**
For you and all mankind.'

The **angel** said: 'In Bethlehem
A **baby's** just been born;
His name is Jesus – and he will be,
Your helper, friend and Lord!

You'll find this little **baby**
In a **stable** made of wood;
He'll be wrapped up in an animal trough
And the place won't smell too good!'

And when the **angel** took a break
A million more turned up,
All shining **bright** and singing strong,
And praising God above.

Then all the **shepherds** left their **sheep**
And ran into the town.
They walked in circles trying to find out
What was going down.

They saw a **stable** lit up **bright**
Just like a Christmas tree.
They all rushed over, crept inside,
And dropped on bended knee.

The parents of the **baby** there,
They looked surprised and stressed.
The **shepherds** grinned; the **baby** stirred,
The **sheep** were not impressed.

All the **shepherds** worshipped him,
Then went back to their **sheep**.
The **baby** in the **stable** yawned
And just went back to sleep!

And since that time of **sheep** and **shepherds**
And **stables** shining **bright**,
The **baby** has become a king –
And what the **angel** said was right. ❑

Matthew/Luke 1 & 2

CHRISTMAS CROWD STORY

This is the story of Christmas
2000 years ago,
With **camels** and **innkeepers** and **shepherds,**
But no sign of any snow.

Come back with me to Palestine
Back to the Middle East,
With **camels, innkeepers** and **shepherds**
And the ancient Prince of Peace.

Late one cold dark night
Some **shepherds** came to town.
They came upon an inn
And nearly broke the front door down.

The **innkeeper** was a gruff old sort
In scruffy clothes and shoes,
'You can't stay here,' he told 'em.
And he didn't half smell of booze.

They'd come to see the **baby**
The one out in the **stable.**
They'd heard that he was special
And didn't think it was a fable.

They went around the back
To the **stable** and the hay
And there amongst the cow dung,
A tiny **baby** lay.

Later on some rich blokes
Came riding on their travels.
They were **wise guys** from the East
And they all rode on **camels**.

The **wise guys** took out presents,
Put them by the baby's bed.
But they didn't call him Trevor*,
They called him Jesus instead.'

They didn't call him Trevor,
But they were right about one thing.
No one forgot the child that night.
He turned out to be a **king**.

*Or Gregor/Ivor/Liam, if you prefer. ❑

STAGE DIRECTIONS

Suitable for an outdoor or large event, the responses are fairly noisy, like those in a pantomime.

Baby
divide audience into two groups
group 1: 'Gurgle, gurgle'
group 2: 'Howl, howl'

Camels
'Brrrr' and make lips vibrate for camel sounds

Innkeeper
cough and clear throat noisily

Shepherds
'Baaa!'

Wise guys
salute and bow quickly

Stable
creaking noises

Matthew/Luke 1 & 2

WHEN HE APPEARED

When he appeared they expected a warrior,
An angel of **light**, or a king.
Not a **tiny** baby, wrapped in straw,
No one expected him.

A fodder trough, a stable and stars,
A teenage **mother**-to-be.
Was this the way to change things?
Was this way it should be?

So he was born, in the dust and the dung,
A **tiny** child of the night.
Shepherds knelt, **eyes wide**
And men from the East saw the **light**.

Both rich and poor were assembled there
Kneeling by the child and his **mother**.
Wise men brought gifts of **spices** and **gold**
The shepherds just brought each other.

Quietly they rose and left that place,
Whispered goodbyes were exchanged in the street.
Wise men went abroad to pass on the **news**
The shepherds went home for a bite to eat.

And two thousand years have since come and gone
And each one remembered the child in the night.
The shepherds and kings have long disappeared,
But the baby lives on, turning darkness to **light**. ❑

STAGE DIRECTIONS

Tiny
hold hands a few inches apart, showing how small the baby was

Mother
pat stomach

Eyes wide
open eyes wide in wonder

Spices
rub fingers and sniff

Gold
'Wow!'

News
whisper to person next to you

Light
point upwards, say 'Ha!' in wonder

Passover was an exciting time of year. All the Jewish **people travelled** to Jerusalem to say thank you to God for helping them to escape from their enemies. For many it was a long journey. The road was very busy with **donkey**s carrying supplies. The **people** walked in family groups. Some of the younger children soon grew hot and tired and were picked up by their parents and put on the **donkeys'** backs.

Mary, Joseph and Jesus **travelled** this journey every year. Jesus was now twelve years old and big enough to guide their **donkey** through the crowds of **people**. Once they reached Jerusalem everyone was heading for one place – the **temple**. The **temple** stood on a great hillside and looked magnificent. Inside it was even more amazing. Many **people** had worked hard to make it a beautiful place for worshipping God. The Jewish teachers sat inside and taught the **people** about God.

This year because there were so many **people** Jesus got separated from his parents in the crowd. But he wasn't **worried** because he knew where the **temple** was. He loved it there and happily guided the **donkey** inside until he found a safe place to tie her up and leave her. Then he crept into the **temple** and joined the celebrations.

Once the Passover celebrations had finished all the **people** returned home. Some were quite sad because it was the end of their holiday, but they collected their baggage and their **donkeys** and **travelled** homewards. Because there were so many **people**, Mary and Joseph didn't notice that Jesus was missing. They thought that he was with some of his friends. However, when night fell and he hadn't rejoined them, Mary started to worry. Their **donkey** was missing too, with all their food and blankets. By dawn Mary and Joseph were **searching** for Jesus everywhere. The more they searched, the more **worried** they became. Finally one of the **people** suggested that they should **travel** back to Jerusalem.

Mary and Joseph ran all the way back to the city. As they came close to the **temple** they saw that there were still lots of **people** in the streets talking and laughing. 'Look over there!' said Joseph, and he pointed to a small brown **donkey** tied to a post. It was theirs – but where was Jesus? Joseph climbed the steps to the **temple** and as he entered the courtyard, he saw Jesus talking to the **temple** teachers in a shaded corner.

When Joseph returned with Jesus to his mother she was quite angry. 'Why have you done this?' she said. 'We were so **worried** about you.' Jesus was puzzled: 'Why were you **searching** for me? Didn't you know I would be in my Father's house?' For Jesus was the Son of God – and he wanted to be close to his Father in the **temple**. Mary didn't quite understand Jesus – but she remembered what he said. ❑

Luke 2

JESUS IN THE TEMPLE

by Soobie Whitfield

STAGE DIRECTIONS

Travel/Travelled
'Trudge, trudge' swing arms

Worried
bite nails

People
'Rhubarb, rhubarb'

Temple
sing 'A-a-amen'

Searching/Searched
hands over eyes, call 'Jesus, Jesus'

Donkey/s
'Ee-aw!'

Matthew 6

TALKING TO GOD

Our Father in heaven
Look up, like a child to a parent.

Hallowed be your name
Outline a large imaginary name plaque hanging above your head.

Your Kingdom come, your will be done
Raise hand to ear as if listening for God's guidance.

On earth as in heaven
Reach down and scoop up some earth, rub it with fingers.

Give us this day our daily bread
Tip away the earth, and with both hands lift up a bread roll and tear it in two, mime eating a chunk.

Forgive us our sins
Cup right hand as if holding sins; look into it then raise it out front and to your right.

As we forgive those who sin against us
Cup left hand, look into it and then hold it out to left, so that you are balancing left and right like scales. Turn both hands over and 'release' all the sins.

Lead us not into temptation
Reach out for something, then stop and retract hand.

But deliver us from evil
Hold hands up to shield face from danger.

For yours is the kingdom
Sweep hands together in front of you as if collecting up a large bundle.

The power
Lift the imaginary bundle up high.

And the glory
Sweep hands across and above you as if smoothing out the sky.

Are yours now and forever
Mime removing watch from wrist and throwing it away.

Amen
Bow heads, with hands clasped. ❏

STAGE DIRECTIONS

One (or more than one) speaker reads the narrative (**bold type**). Another person, or persons, should lead the audience in simple mimed responses (plain text).

One day, as Jesus was **walking** along, he and his friends came to a town and found a long line of people all **walking** along and looking down at the ground. Their faces were very **sad**.

'What's wrong?' Jesus asked, 'Why do they all look so **sad**?'

The people **walked** in silence, looking down at the ground, and the **saddest** of them all was a little old lady. One of Jesus' friends went off to find out what it was all about. He said, 'It's a funeral. That lady is a widow and she's lost her only son. She's all on her own now.'

As they watched the long procession of people **walking** past, it was such a **sad** sight, that Jesus suddenly held up a hand and said, 'Wait a minute, there must be something we can do here.'

He pushed through the **crowd** until he got close to the old lady. 'Please don't cry,' he said, 'it's not over yet.'

The old lady looked confused, but she did stop crying for a moment and watched as Jesus **walked** up to her son as he lay in the coffin. The men carrying the coffin stopped **walking** when they saw Jesus. They put it down. Jesus looked at the boy lying inside it. Jesus looked around at the large **crowd** who were staring at him, he gave a little smile and then he looked down at the boy and said, 'Young man, get up! Now!'

There was a shocked **gasp** from the **crowd** and for a moment nothing happened. Then, slowly the boy opened one eye, then the other. He yawned and coughed and sat up.

The **crowd** gave another **gasp** and some of them fell over, they were so shocked. Suddenly the boy began talking to his mother. The **crowd** gave another **gasp** and even more of them fell over.

The boy climbed out of the coffin and gave his mother big hug. Suddenly everyone was laughing and crying and shouting and running about.

As Jesus and his friends **walked** away they heard people in the **crowd** shouting, ' This is amazing! That man must be some kind of great prophet! God's come to save us!'

Jesus smiled to himself again; he'd spoilt a funeral but saved a life. It was good day. ❑

Luke 7

JESUS SPOILS A FUNERAL

STAGE DIRECTIONS

Sad/saddest
make a sad face

Gasp
'Ha!'

Walked/Walking
make walking movement

Crowd
'That's us!'

Luke 9

UP THE MOUNTAIN

Peter, James and his brother John,
They were all fishing men.
One day Jesus said to them:
'Follow me and you'll catch men!'
Follow me and you'll catch men! x2

So they followed him, became his friend,
Jesus did miracles – lots of them.
Then one day he said to them:
'Come with me and meet my friends.'
Come with me and meet my friends. x2

Peter, John and his brother James
Found themselves on a mountain range.
Suddenly Jesus began to change.
James and John felt very strange!
James and John felt very strange. x2

Jesus' face was all alight,
And his clothes were whiter than white.
He looked dazzling – shining bright.
Peter was shaking, full of fright.
Peter was shaking, full of fright. x2

Just then two more men appeared,
In sandals, cloaks and very long beards.
Peter spoke up, still full of fear,
Said: 'It's really great to be up here!'
It's really great to be up here! x2

'I know,' said Pete, 'let's build three tents
For Jesus and those other two gents.'
A cloud appeared – it didn't make sense.
It came from nowhere, foggy and dense.
It came from nowhere, foggy and dense. x2

It covered them all from head to foot
And then a voice said: 'Listen out!
This is my Son, without a doubt.
I'm pleased with him, so hear him out.'
I'm pleased with him, so hear him out. x2

Peter, James and his brother John
Were terrified and all fell down.
Jesus put his hand on them, said:
'Don't be afraid – everyone's gone!'
Don't be afraid – everyone's gone! x2

They looked up, saw no one around,
And they were glad to get back to town.
Jesus said: 'Don't forget what you saw,
And later on you'll see some more.'
Later on you'll see some more.' x2 ❑

STAGE DIRECTIONS

Get the audience to click their fingers, or clap their hands in a rap rhythm – or use a pre-recorded rap beat.

They should repeat the last line of each verse twice (in **bold type**).

After Jesus had been travelling about a lot, **teaching** people, **healing** them, doing **miracles** and telling **stories**, he decided it was time for his friends to have a go.

First of all he sent out his twelve closest friends. He said, 'Go out to all the people in the nearby villages and towns, **teaching** them, **healing** those who are sick, doing **miracles** and telling them **stories**.'

The disciples were a bit worried about this. They said, 'You're the one who does that, Jesus, not us. You're good at it, why don't you do it? And we'll walk behind you.'

But Jesus said, 'It's your turn, don't take anything with you. Don't bother about packing lots of nice things, or emptying your bank accounts, just go quickly and simply, and wherever you meet people who welcome you, stay with them, **teaching**, **healing**, doing **miracles** and telling **stories**.'

'So people will like us and treat us nicely?'
'Of course.'
'Oh **good**,' said his friends.
'Yes, and when they don't, shake the **dust** off your feet and leave them.'
'What d'you mean, Lord, when they don't? Isn't this going to be easy then?'
'No, but off you go.'
So they went, nervously.

When they got back Jesus' friends were over the moon. 'We did it,' they said. 'It was **fantastic**.'
'Good,' said Jesus, 'I'm sending you out again, this time with a lot more friends. Seventy-two of you.'
'Oh that's **good**,' they said.
'Yes,' said Jesus, 'I'm sending you out like lambs among wolves,'
'Oh dear, that's bad,' they said. 'That's not exactly a word of encouragement, Lord.'

And Jesus said, 'There is a large harvest but only a few people to gather it in. Pray that there will be lots and lots more workers. You'll need more than twelve, more than seventy-two. And remember when you meet people who welcome you, stay with them, **teaching**, **healing**, doing **miracles** and telling **stories**.'

'We like that bit,' they said.
'Yes. And when they don't, shake the **dust** off your feet.'

'We don't like that bit,' they said, but they went off, nervous yet again.

When they got back, Jesus' friends said, 'Lord, it was **fantastic**!'
And Jesus said, '**Good**. But remember, even though you've done amazing things, the most important thing is that you and I are best friends.' ❑

Luke 9 & 10

TEACHING, HEALING, MIRACLES AND STORIES

STAGE DIRECTIONS

Teaching
place hands out, open as if talking

Healing
place hands together as if praying

Miracles
snap fingers

Stories
listen, hand to ear

Good
punch the air

Dust
dust hands off

Fantastic
cheer

Matthew 13

A GOOD HARVEST

A man went out to sow some **seeds**.
He ploughed the field and scattered.
The **seeds** fell on the **ground,**
But some of them got splattered.

Some **seeds** fell on hard **ground.**
The soil was just like **concrete**
And the local **yobs** jumped on them
With big boots on their big feet.

Some **seeds** fell in **thorns.**
'Ouch!' the **seeds** did cry.
But no one came to help them
And soon the **seeds** did die.

Some **seeds** fell on thin **soil**
And couldn't grow too high.
And when the sun came out that **day**,
Those little **seeds** did fry!

A man went out to sow some **seeds**
He ploughed the field and scattered.
Some **seeds** fell on juicy **soil**,
And that's what really mattered.

The **seeds** are just like words from God,
We hear them every **day**.
We see God out there in the world,
At home, at work, at play.

We can be like **concrete** and
God's word will bounce away;
Or we can be like juicy **soil**
And grow a little more each day.

We don't have to be so big
To grow a bit each **day**,
And when the **thorns** and **yobs** come round
We can turn to God and say...

'HELP!' ❑

STAGE DIRECTIONS

Seeds
'Whoosh!' and mime throwing seeds with right hand

Ground
stamp feet on floor once

Concrete
'Dong!' and hit fist on head

Soil
'Squelch, squelch!' and rub fingers together

Yobs
'Oi!!'

Thorns
'Ouch!'

Day
yawn and stretch

Once upon a time two men met for a game of golf. One was a professional player. The other was **not**!
The professional was called **Pete** – Professional **Pete**, they all called him. He was the smoothest, fastest, slickest golfer in the entire district.

The other was **not**. He was called **Sid*** – Slowhand **Sid**. He was the slowest, silliest, most unprofessional golfer in the entire universe.

Professional **Pete** had won every game he'd played in the last ten years. Slowhand **Sid** had **not**.

Well, they met bright and early one morning, shook hands and teed off. **Pete** started with a hole in one. **Sid** did **not**. He started by hitting his **ball** into the bunker. From there he hit into the lake and from there he knocked it into the **rough** and lost it.

So he gave up on that hole and they went on to hole number two. **Pete** won that one too, and in fact, he won the first ten they played. Things were **not** looking good for **Sid**.

Then, suddenly, on the eleventh hole Professional **Pete** sneezed violently just as he hit the **ball** and it shot straight off the tee and into the **rough**. **Sid** was so shocked he almost fainted. Professional **Pete** went straight after the **ball**. He wasn't quite sure how to find a lost **golf ball** as he'd never had to do it before, but he waded into the **rough** and hacked about with his club for a while.

After five minutes **Sid** said, 'Perhaps you'd better give up on this hole.'
But **Pete** said, 'Can't do that.'

After ten minutes **Sid** said, 'Look it's only a **golf ball** and it's about time I won a hole. Give in.'
But **Pete** said, 'No way.'

After half an hour **Sid** said, 'I'm getting hungry.'
Pete said, 'This is my favourite **ball**, I can't abandon it.'

After three hours **Sid** said, 'Bye!'
And **Pete** said, 'You go **Sid**. I've got to stay here till I find that **ball**.'
As he went **Sid** said, 'But you've got nine others, and if you stay here you'll end up losing the whole game and I'll win!'

And that's how Professional **Pete** lost his first game in ten years. 'This **ball** may be little, but it's too important to lose. It doesn't matter how many others I've got, I've never lost a **golf ball** before and I won't lose one now.'

And twelve hours later, as the moon shone down at midnight, **Pete** bent down and found his lost **golf ball**. He smiled to himself, put it safely in his bag and went off home to celebrate. He'd lost the game, but found the **ball**.

*or Steve/Sean/Seamus, if you prefer. ❑

Luke 15

THE PARABLE OF THE LOST GOLF BALL

STAGE DIRECTIONS

Not
'Oh oh!' sounding worried

Rough
'Ouch!'

Golf ball
'Thwack!'

Pete
one half of audience stand

Sid
other half stand

Matthew 13

THE PARABLE OF THE NET

STAGE DIRECTIONS

Net
mime throwing a large net out to sea

Fish
all open and close mouths like goldfish, making *puh* sound

Conkers
mime playing conkers, swinging one at another

Mail
'Post!'

Ticking
'Tick, tick, tick.'

Complaining
'Rhubarb, rhubarb, rhubarb'

Tea
'Sluuuuuuurp'

Jesus once told a story about a fisherman who threw his **net** into the sea then pulled it out and found it was full of **fish**. So the man sat down next to the **net** and sorted out all the good **fish** from all the **bad** fish. That is, he separated all the **fish** he could eat from all the **fish** he couldn't eat.

Nowadays Jesus might tell a story about a man going out for a walk in the autumn leaves, picking up a huge pile of **conkers** and then going home and sorting out all the good strong **conkers** from all the bad rotten **conkers**.

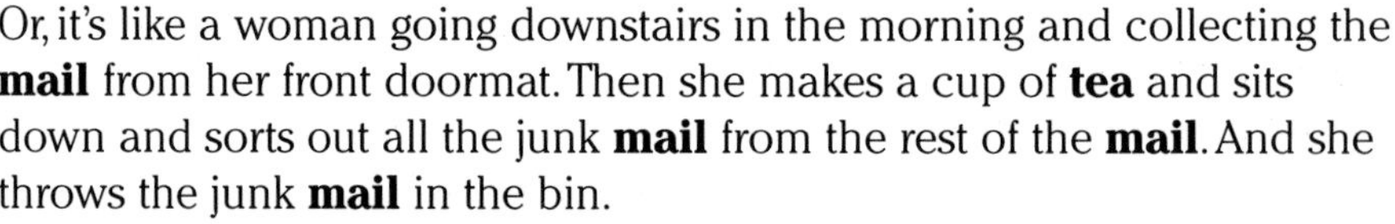

Or, it's like a woman going downstairs in the morning and collecting the **mail** from her front doormat. Then she makes a cup of **tea** and sits down and sorts out all the junk **mail** from the rest of the **mail**. And she throws the junk **mail** in the bin.

Whether it's **fish**, **conkers** or **mail**, it's similar to what will happen when history comes to an end, when the clock of time stops **ticking**. Then God will collect everyone together and separate those who want to be with him from those who don't want to be with him. And there will be a lot of **complaining**, but by then it will be too late. The clock of time will have stopped **ticking**. ❑

Once, there was a **bus stop**. And there were three people waiting at this **bus stop**. First, there was a **posh businessman,** who had a very big house and lots of money.

Then there was the local **churchwarden***. He had a house, and quite a lot of money, but not as much as the **posh businessman**.

The third person at the bus stop was called (**hand to ear**). He was a very **dirty** tramp because he didn't have a house, or any money; he lived in a cardboard box. And he didn't have any friends, because he was so **dirty**.

Well, just then, a gang of **football supporters** went running past the **bus stop**. And these **football supporters** made a lot of noise. Unfortunately these particular **football supporters** were not very nice. They didn't notice the **posh businessman**, the **churchwarden** or (**hand to ear**). But they did see the schoolteacher coming the other way. And as they got to the **bus stop**, the **football supporters** grabbed him, threw him to the ground and stole his wallet, his watch and all his money. Then they ran off, leaving him lying there.

Just then, the **bus** arrived. The **posh businessman** looked at the teacher, then quickly jumped on the **bus**, because he couldn't stand the sight of blood.

The **churchwarden**? Well, he looked at the teacher, then he saw the **businessman** jump on the **bus**, and he decided to do the same, because he was frightened of the **football supporters**.

Meanwhile (**hand to ear**), who was standing on the end, saw the teacher, and felt sorry for him. So he missed the **bus**, went over to the man, and helped him up. Then he gave the teacher 50p, which was all the money he'd got from begging. And even though Sam was very **dirty**, the teacher didn't mind, because he took him to a hospital and made sure that he was OK.

Now, which person was a neighbour to the teacher? Not the **posh businessman**, nor the **churchwarden**. No, the man's neighbour was (**hand to ear**) because he showed him love, and he acted like a friend.

*or similar church officer's title. ❑

GOOD SAM

STAGE DIRECTIONS

Posh businessman
'Oh, I say'

Bus stop/Bus
'Ding! Ding!'

Dirty
'Phaw!'

Churchwarden
shake hands with the person next to you

Football supporters
half of audience shouts for one team, half shouts for another

Hand to ear
'Good Sam, the tramp!'

Like 19

ZACCHAEUS

Once there was a man called Zacchaeus. He was a very **little** man and he couldn't see very much because everyone else was always taller. No one liked him because he was a **tax collector**. Every day he used to sit under his favourite **tree** collecting **taxes** from the people. But he used to force them to pay more **money** than they needed to, so he could keep some for himself. In those days **tax collectors** weren't very nice people.

Now one day a huge crowd of people gathered in the street because a special person was coming to town. While Zacchaeus was counting his **money** under his **tree**, he was suddenly surrounded. Well, he couldn't see a thing because he was too **little**, so he jumped up into his favourite **tree**. From there he could see a man on the road. Well, everyone could see Zacchaeus sitting up in the **tree** and suddenly this man looked up at him and called out: 'Hey, Zacchaeus, come down from that **tree**!'
'Why?' he said, 'I've only just got up here.'
'Because I'm coming to your house for some **tea**.'
'Some **tea**?'
'Yes,' said the man, 'because I want to get to know you.'

Well, the man's name was Jesus, and while he and Zacchaeus had some **tea** they became good friends and Zacchaeus realized that he shouldn't have taken all that **money** from the people.

'I know!' he said, 'I'll give away twice as much as I've taken from people.' (**Cheer**)
'No I won't. (**Aaaah**) I'll give away three times as much. (**Cheer**)
No I won't. (**Aaaah**) I'll give away four times as much!' (**Cheer**)

And that's exactly what he did and from then on Zacchaeus and Jesus were really good friends. ❑

STAGE DIRECTIONS

Tree
'Rustle, rustle'

Money
'Chink, chink'

Tea
'Munch, munch'

Little
crouch down

Taxes/Tax Collector
'Sssss!'

Cheer!/Ahhh!
prepare 'prompt' placards and have volunteers ready to display them

Luke 15

THE SHOPPING TRIP

by Soobie Whitfield

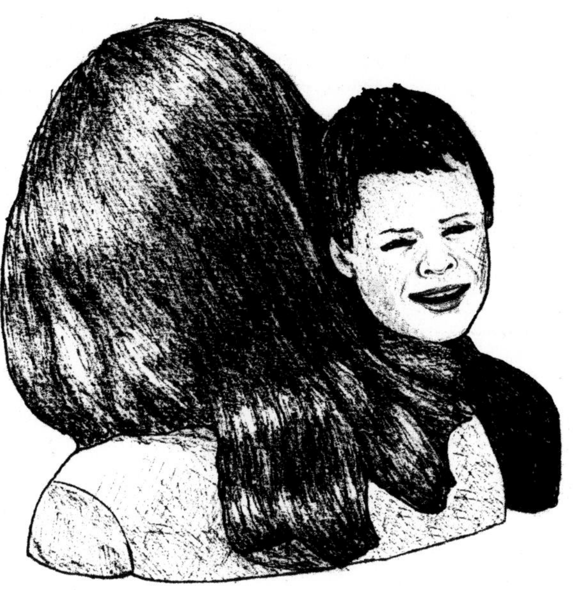

One Saturday Mrs Brown decided to go **shopping**. **Shopping** was always an adventure for Mrs Brown because she had seven **children**: Jimmy, Johnny, Timmy, Tommy, Susie, Sally and Eric. So they got their **shopping** bags and set out for the supermarket. The place was packed solid so Mrs Brown called all the **children** to her and **said**: 'Stay together, hold tight, don't fuss, don't fight.' Then she took out her **shopping** list and asked the children to help. She sent Jimmy, Johnny and Timmy to the freezers to fetch **fish fingers** and **beef burgers**. As they went, she **said**.... And so off they went. She sent Tommy and Susie to the **bread** counter to get a large white sliced **loaf** and a **fruitcake** for Sunday. As they disappeared round the corner she warned them not to get lost. Finally she asked Sally and Eric to get a box of **cornflakes**.

On the way Eric spotted some **chocolate** piled high on the shelves. He was just wandering off to get a closer look when Sally **said**.... Eric shouted back: 'I'll only be a minute,' and disappeared round the corner. Back at the checkout Mrs Brown and the **children** were unloading a very full trolley. Down the conveyor belt went all the **food**. Mrs Brown lifted the heavy **shopping** bags into the trolley, and started to walk towards the car park. As she moved away she looked over her shoulder and **said**....

'STOP!' shouted Sally. 'We've **lost** Eric.' Mrs Brown left her **shopping** and started to search the supermarket for her missing son. She went to the **cornflake** shelf, the **bread** counter, the freezers and the **cake** stand. But she couldn't find him. He was definitely **lost**. So she asked the shop assistant to help her look. Soon the supermarket was full of people looking for **lost** Eric.

Just then Mrs Brown walked round a corner – and there was Eric! She took his hand and when the **children** saw him coming they shouted: 'Where have you been? We were worried. We **lost** you.'

But Mrs Brown just smiled. She picked Eric up in her arms and hugged him. 'I'm very happy,' she told him. 'You were **lost**, but now you're back and we're all together again.' ❑

STAGE DIRECTIONS

Shopping
'Beep, beep!' while miming passing an item over checkout scanner

Food of any kind
'Yum, yum!'

Children
all children cheer

Lost
'OH NO!' hands up to face

Said
'Stay together, hold tight. Don't fuss, don't fight.'

Luke 20

LOTS OF MIRACLE MEN

In the days when Jesus was on the earth, walking about, making friends, meeting people and telling them all about God, there were lots of other people walking around, **pretending** to be important. **Pretending** to be special. **Pretending** to be miracle men. **Pretending** to be **messengers** from God. Now the Pharisees, who were like priests and ministers back then, they went around asking these people difficult questions to find out if they were really God's **messengers**, or if they were just **pretending**.

When they saw a man preaching on a street corner they might go up to him and ask a question like this: 'Should we pay taxes to **Caesar** or not?'

And if the man said: 'Yes.' they would not listen to him, because they didn't like **Caesar**. And if the man said 'No.' then they would sneak off to **Caesar** and the Romans and tell them to arrest the man. And if the answer was 'I don't know', then they'd just laugh at the person for **pretending** to be a messenger from God. You see, they didn't really want to know the answer; they just wanted to **trick** people.

So, one day they went up to Jesus and asked him: 'Should we pay taxes to **Caesar** or not?'

Now Jesus was very clever and he knew they were just trying to **trick** him, like they **tricked** everyone else. So Jesus asked them for some money. He held it up and said: 'Whose picture is stamped on this money?'
The Pharisees looked at the money and said, '**Caesar's** of course.'
So Jesus replied, 'Well then, pay **Caesar** what belongs to **Caesar** and pay God what belongs to him.'

The Pharisees looked puzzled and didn't know what to say to that. They were well and truly stumped. 'Drat!' they muttered. 'We'll have to think of a new question for **tricking** people with now.'

And some of them realized that Jesus wasn't **pretending**. He really was a **messenger** from God, and one or two of them even began to realize the truth. He wasn't just a **messenger**. He was God's very own son. ❑

STAGE DIRECTIONS

Caesar
all stand up and bow, and quickly sit down again

Pretending
give a deliberate sly wink

Messengers
place hands to mouth and shout 'Listen!'

Trick
snigger behind hands

Matthew 25

DOING THEIR BEST

There was once a man who owned a leisure centre. It was the best leisure centre around, and it was run by the man's three **assistants**: Dirk, Digby and Dougal. One day the man decided to go on a **trip** around the world. So he called in the three **assistants** and said to them: 'I'm going on a **trip** around the world – and I want you to look after my leisure centre for me.'

He put Dirk in charge of the **swimming pool**. Then he put Digby in charge of the **trampolines**, the table tennis and the **coke** machines. Dougal was put in the toilets – to look after them. Then the owner told them to do their **best** and he waved goodbye and left on his **trip**.

It took Dirk ten seconds to decide what to do. It took Digby ten minutes to decide what to do. It took Dougal ten days to decide what to do – but he got there in the end!

Three weeks later the owner returned. 'Hello!' he said to his **assistants**. 'I had a nice **trip**. Now, what have you been doing with my leisure centre?'

Dirk jumped up and said: 'I cleaned the **swimming pool** every day, put in a brand new inflatable shark, rescued three people in difficulties and I made £500 profit.'

'Well done,' said the owner.

Dougal jumped forward and said: 'I cleaned the toilets every day, put in some brand new fluorescent toilet paper and some delicious chocolate soap, and I charged everyone 20p a minute to go in. Here's the profit – £200.'

The owner was very pleased when he saw they had done their best. Then he turned to Digby, who said: 'I locked up the **trampolines** so the children couldn't get at them, then I sat on the table-tennis table and drank all the **coke** – it was very tasty.'

'What?' said the owner. 'You mean you wasted all that time and money. Was that all you could do?'

'Well, I think you work people too hard,' said Digby, 'and I felt like having a rest, and anyway. I wanted to look after the **swimming pool**, not the **trampolines**.'

The owner was so angry that he gave Digby the sack and threw him outside. But he promoted his other two **assistants** and he gave them both a pay rise because he knew he could trust them always to do their **best**. ❑

STAGE DIRECTIONS

Coke
'Fizzzz!' and mime opening can

Trip
'Oops!'

Best
punch the air and say 'Yea!'

Assistants
'Yes sir!'

Trampolines
'Boiing!'

Swimming pool
'Splosh!'

Mark 12

THE WIDOW'S MITE

STAGE DIRECTIONS

Rich
rub fingers and say: 'Money, money, money, money.'

Poor
mime pulling a tiny coin from pocket – hold it up between finger and thumb

Servants
bow

Talking
'Rabbit, rabbit!'

Box
'Rattle, clink!'

Whistle
all whistle

This story is about two people, one who was **rich** and one who was poor. The **rich** person was a man who had a big house and lots of **servants**. One day he decided to go to church to put some money into the collection **box**. So he called his **servants** and told them to bring three large bags of gold coins. They they all set off **talking** together.

The **rich** man was very happy that day and he started to **whistle** as he walked along. The **servants** weren't quite so happy because the money bags were heavy but they **whistled** as well, because the **rich** man told them to.

As they got near the church they saw a crowd of people **talking**. The **rich** man carried on **whistling** and went over to them. They were all **talking** to Jesus, but the **rich** man wasn't really interested so he took his **servants** into the church. Inside there was a large, wooden collection **box**. The **servants** had a rest while the man picked up the first bag, and one by one he put the gold coins into the **box**. When the bag was empty he picked up the second one and put more coins into the **box**. He enjoyed doing this and **whistled** loudly. After he had put the third bag into the **box** they all got up and went outside. On their way out they bumped into a **poor** widow. She was very, very, very **poor** – but the **rich** man hardly saw her and he and his **servants** walked home happily.

The **poor** widow crept quietly to the **box** and put in two small pennies. It was all she had and it only took two seconds to do it, then she quickly ran outside again. But Jesus had been watching everything, and he turned to all the people who were **talking**, and he said to them: 'That **poor** widow put a lot more in the **box** than the **rich** man did because she put in everything that she had.' ❑

Matthew 21

THE TRIUMPHAL ENTRY

by Keith Fraser-Smith

It was the last visit Jesus would make to Jerusalem. He told two of his **followers** to go and pick up transport from Peter's Rent-a-**Donkey**. Jesus got onto the donkey and **rode** it into the city. His **followers** followed him. When he got close to Jerusalem a big **crowd** began to gather. Some people cut down palm branches and threw them on the road in front of the **donkey** that Jesus was **riding**. They took off their coats too and threw them in front of the **donkey**. Then they started shouting '**Hosanna** to the Son of David, blessed is he who comes in the name of the Lord. **Hosanna** in the highest.'

The **donkey** kept walking. Jesus kept **riding**. They weren't afraid of the **crowds**. They kept on shouting: '**Hosanna**!'

And so Jesus came into Jerusalem **riding** on a **donkey**, followed by his **followers**, and cheered on by the **crowds**.

Jesus was very popular. But later that week it would all change. There would be no **donkey**. His **followers** would run away. And the **crowds**? They would **boo** him. Jesus became the most unpopular person in Jerusalem and a terrible thing happened to him. He was put to death by being nailed to a wooden cross. ❑

STAGE DIRECTIONS

Followers
stamp up and down

Riding/Rode
riding movements

Donkey
'Ee-aw, ee-aw!'

Crowd/s
'Hooray! Hooray!'

Hosanna
pretend to wave flags

Boo
all shout 'Boo!'

Matthew 21

PALM SUNDAY CROWD STORY

STAGE DIRECTIONS

Suitable for a large-scale event. The responses are fairly noisy, like those in a pantomime.

'Can't do that!'
divide the crowd in two to respond:
1. 'Oh yes, you can!';
2. 'Oh no, you can't!'

Donkey
all shout:
'Which donkey?'

Grumble/grumbling
divide the crowd into four groups and say in sequence:
1. 'Mumble, mumble,'
2. 'Rhubarb, rhubarb,'
3. 'Leave it out,'
4. 'Shut that door.'

Picture the scene: Jesus and his followers have been travelling for a long time and they're worn out. So Jesus gets his disciples together and says: 'Listen mates, I think it's time for the **donkey**. The one you're gonna get from that town over there.'

'Hang on, Guv,' said the disciples. 'We can't just walk in and pinch one. We **can't do that**!'

So Jesus sat them all down and said: 'Now, look, I've had this plan worked out for a while. Two of you are gonna nip into the town, and when you see the **donkey** – the one in the town – it'll be next to another **donkey**. The one with the other **donkey**. Oh don't worry. You'll know it when you see it!'

Now the disciples weren't so sure and they started having a **grumble**.

'Look, it's no use **grumbling**,' said Jesus. 'It's all worked out. You two nip in there and bring back the first **donkey** you see. Don't start that again! If you get any bother just say: "The master needs it."'

So they nipped off into the town, and sure enough they saw the two animals tied up. So one of them kept watch while the other untied them. Suddenly two massive bruisers appeared, looking very mean. One of them shouted: 'Hey! You **can't do that**!'

'No you can't,' said the men, 'cos that's our **donkey**!' The two big men looked as if they were gearing up for a fight, so the disciples quickly chipped in: 'The master needs it!' And off they went, leaving the two bruisers standing there **grumbling**.

As soon as they got back, Jesus got on the **donkey**. Er, the one on the left. And he rode into Jerusalem in front of huge crowds of people, all shouting and singing and praising God. Well, most of the people had a great time, but a few of them – the priests and religious leaders – all they could do was **grumble**. But nobody cared, because all they wanted to do was see Jesus, for he was the King. ❑

Matthew 26

COMMUNION RAP

On the night before Friday, not a moment too **soon**
Jesus took his friends to an upper room.
They had a good **meal** and a real nice chat
And this is what happened right after that.

There was a hunk of **bread** on the **table** there
So Jesus picked it up and he said a prayer.
Then he **broke** it in pieces and he said to them
Take it and eat it 'cause I'm your friend.

There was a cup of **wine** on the **table** too
So he lifted that up and he said 'Thank you.'
Then he passed it around, the **wine** was red
And when they'd all had a drink this is what he said:

'This **wine** is like blood pumping round my heart
And it's going to be the sign of a brand new start.
My body will be **broken**, just like this **bread**
And my blood will be spilled and I will be dead.

'You'll **see** it happen before your very eyes,
But three days later you'll **see** me rise.
Death won't hold me – I'll break the chains
And **soon** I promise I'll be back again.

And when you meet together from time to time
Remember me with **bread** and **wine**
This **bread** is my body and my blood is this **wine**.
Take it with **respect** as a sign that you're mine!' ❑

STAGE DIRECTIONS

Bread
sniff as if smelling fresh bread

Wine
mime holding up a cup of wine

Table
knock on something wooden

Soon
check watch on wrist

See
look amazed and shocked

Respect
give each other five

Meal
make eating sounds

Broke/broken
mime breaking open a bread roll

Matthew 27 & Luke 23

GOOD FRIDAY

It felt like the longest day in **history**.
Jesus had been arrested and taken to **prison**.
Everybody had turned against him and his friends had **run away**.

Jesus had to go through ten horrible experiences all on his own.

1. They took Jesus to the priest's house. There they asked him lots of questions and told lies about him.

2. The soldiers took him outside, hit him and spat in his face.

3. They took Jesus to Pontius Pilate, the man in charge of executions. There they accused him of saying things against God.

4. They took him to Herod the king. Herod made Jesus wear a purple robe, laughed at him and made fun of him.

5. They sent Jesus back to Pontius Pilate who ordered his soldiers to whip Jesus. The soldiers also made a crown out of long thorns and they pressed it onto Jesus' head.

6. They took Jesus out to a large crowd of people who all wanted him to be crucified. They set a guilty man free and decided to kill Jesus in his place.

7. The soldiers made Jesus carry a huge wooden cross up a long hill to a place called Golgotha. The cross was so heavy that he fell down on the way.

8. They nailed Jesus to the cross and crucified him in front of all the people. The crowds laughed, shouted and jeered at him.

9. The soldiers stole his clothes and played games to decide who would have his coat.

10. After many painful hours on the cross Jesus prayed for all the people – and then he died.

It felt like the longest day in **history**.
Jesus had been arrested and taken to **prison**.
Everybody had turned against him and his friends had **run away**.

He had never done anything wrong, never hurt anyone, never stolen anything, never even told a lie.
But the people killed him – as if he was guilty.
He died in our place.
He died for you and me. ❑

STAGE DIRECTIONS

History
open hands like a book and blow dust

Prison
'Clang!' and clap hands together

Run away
turn away and put hands up, rejecting

Numbers 1 to 10
hold up appropriate number of fingers

Acts 1

THE COMMISSION

Our story starts quite a few days after Jesus had risen from the dead. He called all his disciples together and took them for a **walk**. They started going **up** a **hill** together.

As they **walked**, Jesus told them that God had a very special **gift** for them, to help them live their lives. But first he had to leave them. They wondered where he might go. **On holiday? On a ship? On a journey?**

So as they **walked** to the top of this **hill** Jesus told them about the **gift**. He was going to **leave** so that they could have this **gift**. The disciples wondered what it might be. **Was it some food? Or a game? Or a car?** Jesus said the **gift** was the Holy Spirit. He told the disciples to go all over the world telling people about God, praying for them and doing miracles.

Well, they were all tired now from the **walk** and the disciples didn't feel like doing any miracles right at that moment. They wanted to sit down on the **hill**. At the top of the **hill** Jesus told them they had to wait for the gift in Jerusalem, and then he said goodbye to them all. The disciples were very sad because they didn't want Jesus to **leave**. But he stood on the **hill** and suddenly began to go **up** in the air. **Was he flying?** He was being lifted **up** to heaven by God.

The disciples were amazed and stayed on the **hill** a long time, looking **up**, and thinking about Jesus **leaving**. Then two men in white appeared and said, 'Why are still standing here looking **up**? You've seen Jesus **leave** – but he will be back one day.' So the disciples turned away and **walked** back down the **hill**, back home to wait for the **gift** that Jesus had promised. The **gift** of the Holy Spirit. ❑

STAGE DIRECTIONS

Hill
pant and puff

Walk/walked
steps on the spot

Gift
'It's for you!'

Leave
'Bye!' and wave

Answer to any question
'No!'

Up
look up sharply

Acts 2

THE DAY OF PENTECOST

It all began a few days after **Jesus** had gone back up to heaven. The disciples were feeling very sad and **frightened**. They met together every day to talk about things, but no one really knew what to do. **Jesus** had been their friend and their guide and now they felt lost and **frightened** without him. Peter tried hard to encourage them, but they all felt very alone and very **frightened**.

On one particular day they were all together in one room sitting and praying quietly when all of a sudden it felt like there was a strong **wind** blowing. Peter ran to the window and looked out – but it was all peaceful outside. The **wind** was blowing in the house!

Then a **fire** appeared floating in the air in the middle of the room, and little flames came out of the **fire** and touched each person. But no one got burnt because the **fire** and the rushing **wind** were from **Jesus** and it meant they were being filled with God's Spirit. And instead of feeling **frightened** they started to feel fantastic.

Then the **wind** and the **fire** stopped and they began to talk in lots of different **languages**, as God gave them each a new **language** to speak. So, as they chattered away they walked outside where there were lots of people from all different countries. And suddenly they realized that the **languages** they were speaking were the same as the **languages** of all these different countries. So they told the people all about **Jesus**, and more than three thousand people decided to become Christians that day. And that was the start of the Church. ❑

STAGE DIRECTIONS

Frightened
'HELP!'

Fire
'Crackle, crackle' and waggle fingers like flames

Wind
whistling sounds

Jesus
cheer

Language
'Jibber, jabber' while nodding head from side to side

Acts 9

SAUL AND THE BRIGHT LIGHT

There was a man called Saul, who wasn't very tall, and he didn't like Christian folk.
He'd give you a **fright** if you'd seen the **light** and it really was no joke.

One day he said, 'Let's go to Damascus instead,' and he climbed aboard his horse.
He rode off hard, with a big **bodyguard**, but something changed his course.

They'd not gone far when something bizarre gave them all a **fright**.
The horses stopped and the **bodyguard** dropped as the sky grew very bright.

'Who are you, Lord?' said trembling Saul. 'What's this **light** above?'
'I am Jesus,' said the **voice**. 'And I thought I'd give you a shove.'

'When you go round putting Christians down, it's me you're really after.'
And the **voice** went on, clear and strong, 'Saul, you couldn't be dafter.'

'You may think it odd, but you can't beat God. So get up and listen, mate.
Go **straight** into the city and **straight** to a street called **Straight**.'

When Paul got up, he was all shook up; his face was scared and white.
His **bodyguard** was shaking too; they'd all had quite a **fright**.

Saul looked around but there was no sound, all was dark and grim.
He said, 'I can't see, a thing.' The **light** had blinded him.

In a street called **Straight** they met a mate, Judas he was called.
They stayed with him till a man popped in, looking for brother Saul.

The man came to call to pray for Saul that he might see the **light**
To Saul's surprise, scales fell off his eyes and he could see all right.

And soon brother Saul became St Paul, now he'd seen the **light**.
And he did his best to tell all the rest about his new friend Jesus Christ. ❑

STAGE DIRECTIONS

Bodyguard
flex muscles

Light
shield eyes and look up

Voice
place hand to ear

Straight
shoot arm out straight

Fright
look very scared

Acts 9

PAUL'S NARROW ESCAPE

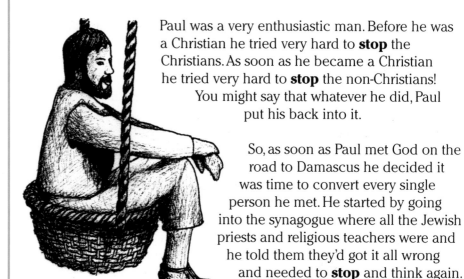

Paul was a very enthusiastic man. Before he was a Christian he tried very hard to **stop** the Christians. As soon as he became a Christian he tried very hard to **stop** the non-Christians! You might say that whatever he did, Paul put his back into it.

So, as soon as Paul met God on the road to Damascus he decided it was time to convert every single person he met. He started by going into the synagogue where all the Jewish priests and religious teachers were and he told them they'd got it all wrong and needed to **stop** and think again. Oh dear!

They went **bananas**. All the priests and the religious teachers couldn't work out what had happened. They said, 'Wait a minute! **Stop**! Isn't this the same man who wanted to kill all the Christians? What's he doing trying to convert us then? He must be **bananas**!'

This went on for a few days and Paul's preaching was so good that soon they all had a big **argument**, and after the big **argument** they decided that the best thing to do was to kill Paul. So they got together and made up a **plan**. Every night they would secretly watch the **gates** of the city waiting for Paul to leave so they could pounce on him and catch him. But Paul found out about their **plan** and even though they watched the **gates** every night, they didn't catch him.

Instead, Paul's friends came up with their own **plan**. Late one night they tied a rope to a large **basket**, and then they climbed up onto the wall far away from the city **gates**, and they put Paul inside the **basket** and lowered him down to safety. Then Paul ran away from the city and went out into the desert and lived there for a while. ❑

STAGE DIRECTIONS

Stop
hold up hands like a traffic cop

Bananas
all pull funny faces

Argument
'Quiet!'

Plan
mime holding a bit of paper and turn it round one way then the other, trying to read it

Gates
'Squeak – clang!'

Basket
'Creak!'

Acts 16

THE PRISON BREAKOUT

Some people are sent to **prison** because they have done something wrong, like stealing, or spying or smashing things up.

But sometimes people are sent to **prison** because of the things they believe – like Paul and Silas.

They were arrested one day for helping a fortune teller. She made a lot of money by predicting the future, and when she met Paul and Silas she could see immediately that they were servants and friends of God. So Paul prayed for her and set her free from the evil spirit that made her predict the future. The woman felt a lot better, but the men who made money out of her were not happy at all. They grabbed hold of Paul and Silas and **dragged** them into the town square. They told the officials in charge of the city that Paul and Silas were causing trouble and should be punished. So the officials grabbed them, and ordered them to be whipped. Paul and Silas were injured badly. Then the officials **dragged** them into **prison**, but Paul and Silas didn't give up, instead they sang songs to God in the **prison**.

Near midnight there was a loud rumbling sound and the ground began to **shake** and **shake** and **shake**. The jailer ran in and cried, 'What's going on?'

There was a very big earthquake, so big that it **shook** the doors off the prison, and there was nothing to stop the prisoners from running away.

'Oh no!' said the jailer, and he **shook** with terror. 'This is terrible. I've let all the **bad guys** out. It's all my fault.'

Of course, it wasn't really his fault but he felt so bad about it that he picked up a sword and got ready to kill himself. Then he a heard a voice yell, '**Wow**! Stop! Wait a minute!'

The jailer picked up a torch and looked into the **prison**. All the **bad guys** were still there, and Paul and Silas were there too.

'We're still here,' said Paul. 'It's OK, don't hurt yourself.'
The jailer was amazed. He'd heard about Paul and Silas and knew they believed in God.
'Tell me about this God of yours,' said the jailer. 'I want to know how to be saved by him.'
So Paul and Silas started to tell him, but he said, '**Wow**! Stop! Wait a minute!'
And he **dragged** them over to his house.
'Tell all my family about him too!' he said.

And so that night Paul and Silas told the jailer and all his family about God and every one of them believed in God and decided to follow him. ❑

STAGE DIRECTIONS

Dragged
pull at your own collar, as if dragging yourself away

Wow!
'Wow!'

Prison
mime turning a key in a lock and say 'Click, clunk!'

Shake/shook
all tremble

Bad guys
all say 'Gurrr!' and look mean

Ephesians 6

PUTTING ON THE ARMOUR

When a Roman soldier used to go into battle, he first put on special armour for protection.

First, he put on a good strong **belt** over his leather tunic.
Second, he put on a plate of **armour** across his chest.
Third, he put on **shoes** for marching and running.
Fourth, he carried a big **shield** to protect himself from the enemy.
Fifth, he put on his metal **helmet**.
Sixth, he picked up his **sword** for fighting the battle.

Now, in God's armour, the **belt** we can put around our waist is truth: we can try to be honest and open.
The **armour** on our chest is the new life we have, forgiven and accepted and changed by God.
For our **shoes**, we have a desire to tell other people about Jesus – that's what keeps us on the move.
Our **shield** is our trust in God. He will protect us like he protected David against Goliath the giant.
Next, the **helmet**. God has rescued us. He sent Jesus to come and save us from bad things. And knowing that we have been rescued by him helps to keep our minds safe and protected in the same way that wearing a **helmet** helps to keep our heads safe and protected.
And the Bible is like a **sword** – we don't hit people with it, but we can tell people what's inside it. That will help us through each day and help us fight our way through the problems we might face.

So **first**, the **belt** of truth.
Second, the **armour** of being right with God.
Third, the **shoes** of telling other people about Jesus.
Fourth, the big **shield** of our trust in God.
Fifth, the **helmet** of being rescued.
And **sixth**, the **sword** of the Bible for fighting the battle.

And **seventh**, we can talk to God about everything we do and everyone we know. And that's the last weapon we have on top of… (*Say this list quickly*) the **belt**, the **armour**, the **shoes**, the **shield**, the **helmet**, the **sword** – the weapon of prayer.

So one more time: the **belt**, the **armour**, the **shoes**, the **shield**, the **helmet**, the **sword** and… the weapon of prayer.

Amen! ❑

STAGE DIRECTIONS

First, second, third etc.
hold up appropriate number of fingers and shout number aloud, e.g. **First**: 'One!'

Belt
mime doing up a big belt

Armour
slap hands on stomach or chest

Shoes
mime putting on shoes

Shield
mime holding up a shield and dodging around behind it

Helmet
pretend to pull on a helmet

Sword
pretend to hold up a large sword

Some drop litter, leave graffiti on a seat.
Some trash bottles, leaving glass out on the street.
It ain't just a mess, it's about self-worth
And it's all about the way we treat the good ol' earth.
And its' all about the way we treat the good ol' earth. x2

All of us are crazy, we waste so much.
All of us are lazy and out of touch.
We don't realize the mountain of things
That ends up sitting in our own waste bins.
That ends up sitting in our own waste bins. x2

We throw stuff away or we keep it in a hoard.
We buy it in the first place just because we are bored.
Some people say: 'Gotta change our ways.
The earth is like an old man in his last days.'
The earth is like an old man in his last days. x2

We all blame each other, and we say it with sorrow,
But we live as if there was no tomorrow.
Some people say that the future can be bright.
We can all live well if we all live right.
We can all live well if we all live right. x2

Some people say it's too late to save the planet.
Someone's already done it, the one who first began it.
Whatever you say, whatever you discover,
Be kind to the planet and be kind to one another.
Be kind to the planet and be kind to one another. x2 ❑

Stewardship

THIS OL' EARTH

STAGE DIRECTIONS

Get the audience to click their fingers as you rap the following reading, and ask them to repeat the last line of each verse twice. You may like to run through these at the beginning.

Money

A PURPLE PATCH

There was a **purple** man, lived in a **purple** land
With a **purple** wife and cat, **purple** house and welcome mat.
He bought a ticket one day, for the lottery to play,
It wasn't **purple** though, but he was desperate to know
If his **purple** luck was in, if he might just win.

He picked six numbers with no link, wrote them all in **purple** ink,
Then watched on Saturday night, to see if he'd chosen right.
Well, as the lottery began there was a very loud bang!
The **purple** man saw **red** because his television set
Went all **green** and **yellow** – he was not a happy fellow.

He felt very **browned** off, though his wife just gave a cough.
She dragged him to the neighbours, and explained about his labours.
So they let the **Purples** in, not believing they would win.
But from feeling rather **blue**, the **Purples** turned a different hue.
Their luck had come around, they'd won ten million pound!

Now their neighbours turned bright **green** 'cause they hadn't won a bean.
The **purple** man scooped the lot, and they'd not won a jot.
So they waited in a thicket till the man came with his ticket
To claim his **purple** win, then they killed and buried him!
And when his **purple** wife came there, they did the same to her!

And though it wasn't cricket, they made off with the ticket,
Got the cash that day, and then tried to run away.
But the boys in **blue** were slick and they locked them in the nick.
So the moral of this mishap is that money is a big trap.
It can help you when you're needy. It can also make you greedy. ❑

STAGE DIRECTIONS

When any colour is mentioned, point to that colour if you can see it anywhere.